Happy 1999 Christmas

love Jenny & Martin.

xxx

# FANTASTIC
# OPTICAL ILLUSIONS
# &
# PUZZLES

LAGOON BOOKS, LONDON

**Series Editor:** Simon Melhuish
**Editor:** Heather Dickson
**Research:** Hannah Robson & Simon Melhuish
**Page design and layout:** Linley Clode
**Cover design:** Gary Sherwood

Published by:
LAGOON BOOKS
PO BOX 311, KT2 5QW, UK

ISBN:   1-89971 -240-2

Printed in Singapore.

# Fantastic Optical Illusions & Puzzles

LAGOON
BOOKS

**OTHER TITLES AVAILABLE FROM LAGOON BOOKS:**

# INTRODUCTION

This collection brings together the greatest, the most dazzling and the most visually intriguing of the world's wonderful optical illusions and puzzles. Impossible structures, straight lines that appear to bend, images that appear to spin, and colours that just don't exist - they are all here in this elegant little volume.

Many other titles are available in this excellent range that explore all that is intriguing and puzzling in this world!

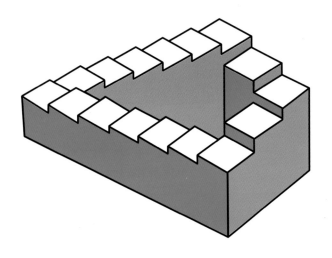

# THE IMPOSSIBLE STAIRCASE — IT KEEPS ON RISING!

Known as the 'Penrose stairs', after its originator,
this is one of the all-time classic optical illusions.

**CAN YOU STARE AT THIS DESIGN WITHOUT YOUR EYES CONSTANTLY SHIFTING OUT OF FOCUS?**

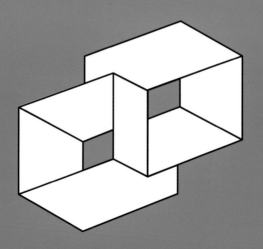

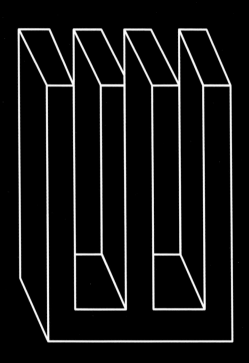

# WHAT'S WRONG WITH THIS?

Amazingly the top has four arms!

4

## WHICH DOT CAN NEVER
## ESCAPE FROM THE MAZE?

The dot on the left. The fact that a line drawn
from this dot crosses the twisted circle an odd
number of times proves that this is so.

# WHICH ANIMAL DO YOU SEE?

The long ears of the rabbit are instantly transformed into the beak of a duck when the book is turned on its side.

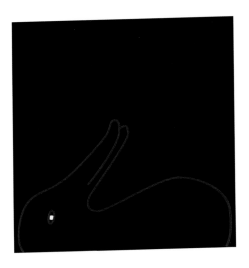

Is the small arch in front of the large arch or underneath it?

# SPOT THE OPTICAL ILLUSION IN THE FRENCH FLAG.

Although it's difficult to spot, the white area is smaller than the blue and the red areas to counteract the Irradiation Effect, which makes the light areas look larger than areas of concentrated colour.

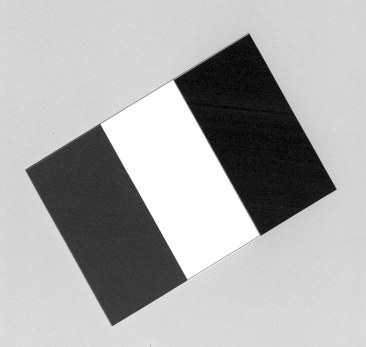

10

# TWO IMAGES VIE FOR ATTENTION IN THIS PICTURE. WHICH GRABS YOURS?

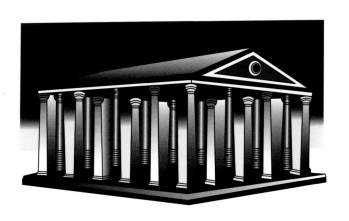

ON FIRST GLANCE THE TEMPLE LOOKS TO BE A
PERFECT EXAMPLE OF GREEK ARCHITECTURE, BUT ON
CLOSER INSPECTION THERE IS A COLOSSAL MISTAKE.

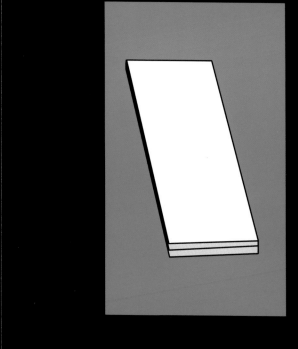

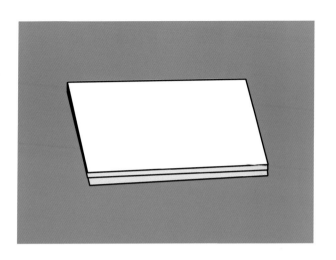

The parallel drawings
have the effect of
making the plank on
the left seem oblong
and the one above
square, but amazingly
the planks are exactly
the same size. If you
don't believe it, get out
a ruler and measure
them for yourself!

# IS THE POOL BALL NEARER THE TOP OR THE BOTTOM OF THE TRIANGLE?

It's bang in the middle but you'll need a ruler to prove it to yourself — your judgement is distorted by the larger area of space below the ball.

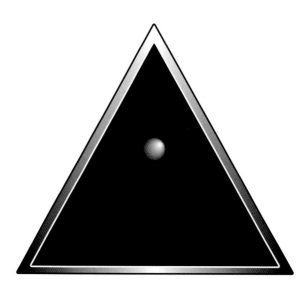

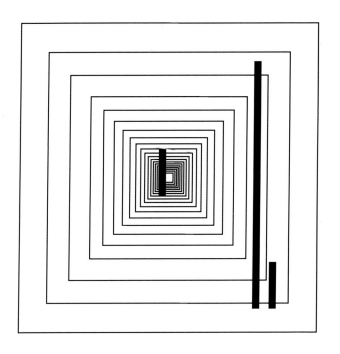

# WHICH IS THE TALLER OF THE TWO SHORTER STICKS?

Actually both short sticks are exactly
the same height but the brain
unconsciously elongates the stick in the
background, making it look taller.

# WHICH DO YOU READ FIRST,
# THE LETTERS OR THE NUMBERS?

The way we interpret characters, depends on the context. In this diagram, the w of Two can also be the e of One or the 3 of 0, 1, 2, 3.

# FOCUS ON THIS SKULL FOR AT LEAST 20 SECONDS THEN IMMEDIATELY STARE AT A BLANK SHEET OF WHITE PAPER. WHAT DO YOU SEE?

18

# WHAT IS WRONG WITH THIS PICTURE OF A FACE?

Turn it upside down and you'll see! The brain reads the inverted picture as correct but turn the book around and we see the lips are upside down and the eyes are the wrong way round.

20

PROBABLY THE
BEST KNOWN OPTICAL
ILLUSION IN THE WORLD.
HOW DOES IT WORK?

22

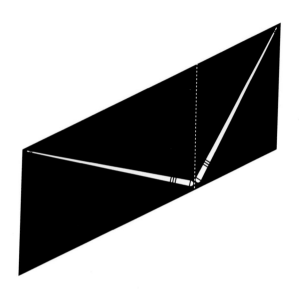

# WHICH POOL CUE IS LONGEST?

However good your aim, they're both the same.
This illusion is known as Sandor's Parallelogram.

# ARE THESE LINES PARALLEL OR NOT?

Although they appear to bend and bulge,
the lines are straight as arrows.
This is an example of a Wundt Illusion, showing the
effect of angular lines on parallel lines.

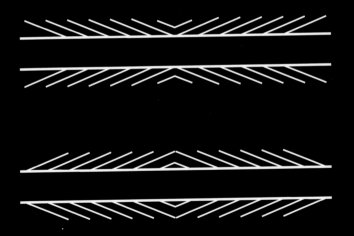

# WHO DO YOU SEE?

"My wife and my mother-in-law" by W.E. Hill (1915).

**A**

**B**

**C**

# WHICH IS GREATEST, THE DISTANCE BETWEEN POINTS A AND B, OR B AND C?

Once you've decided, you'd better get that ruler out again!

# Is this a perfect square?

It certainly is, but the concentric circles make you believe otherwise.

28

# CAN YOU SEE ANY COLOURS WHEN YOU STARE AT THIS PICTURE?

It's common to see coloured diamonds at right-angles to the lines. This is known as the Luckiesh-Moss figure but no-one knows why it occurs!

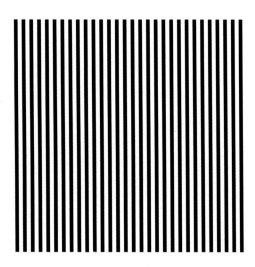

## WHAT DO YOU SEE?

The word FAST can
be read in the open
spaces between the
shapes but it's difficult
to spot because we
are accustomed to
reading closed letters
of the alphabet.

# FRASER'S SPIRAL

A fabulous illusion because long after the brain realises this is not a spiral at all, it continues to see it as such! In fact it's a series of concentric circles on a background which draws the eye towards the centre.

# WHAT'S WRONG WITH THIS ELEPHANT?...
## ...STUMPED?

What may look like the perfect specimen
of an elephant on first glance, is in fact a
legless jumbo, for although it has four feet,
they are not connected to its body in any way.

34

# YOU ARE ON ROAD 1 AND GO UNDER A BRIDGE. WHICH ROAD SHOULD YOU BE ON WHEN YOU COME OUT AT THE OTHER SIDE?

If you're on road 3 you've taken the wrong turning. You should come out on road 2 which is a continuation of 1.
This is an example of a Poggendorf Illusion.

BY ROTATING THE BOOK FROM LEFT TO RIGHT, GREY LINES FROM THE CENTRE OF THE CIRCLE CREATE THE ILLUSION OF MOVEMENT.

# A real world illusion — Why does the moon appear larger the lower it is in the sky?

When the moon is low it can be compared in size to easily recognisable objects on the landscape and looks huge, but when it's high in the sky there's nothing to liken it to and it therefore seems smaller.

38

# WHICH IS THE BIGGER SQUARE?

Surprisingly they are the same size. Light areas look larger than areas of concentrated colour because of the impression they have on our retinas.

# IN WHICH DIRECTION ARE THESE WOMEN LOOKING?

Although their facial features suggest otherwise,
both women are looking in exactly the same
direction. If you cover their lower faces with your
hand, you can see that their eyes are identical.

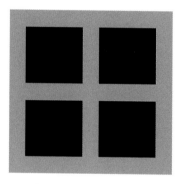

# WHICH WINDOW IS A PERFECT SQUARE?

Window B has equal sides. People often mistake window A, which has shorter vertical sides, as the perfect square as we are inclined to over-estimate the length of vertical lines when compared to horizontal ones.

**B**

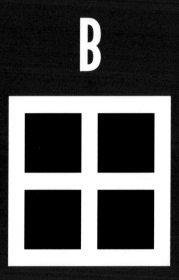

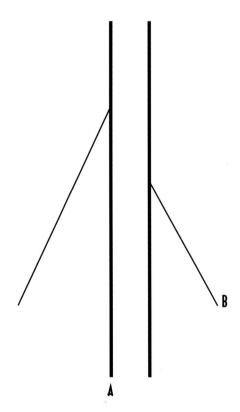

A

B

# WHERE DO LINES A AND B MEET?

Check with a ruler!

# Are the balustrades black or white?

Where the balustrade is symmetrical, it appears to
be in the foreground. If you look at the top of the
picture, the balustrade seems black whereas if you look at
the bottom of the picture, it looks white.

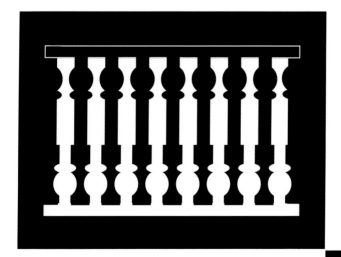

44

They are giving away free pizzas at papa Luigi's Pizzeria. Which would greedy Uncle Tom take, the cheese or the tomato pizza?

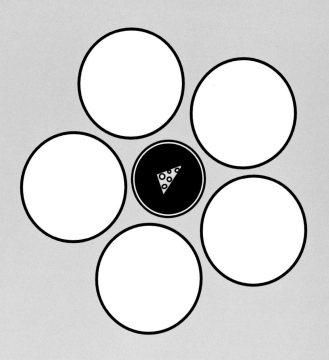

He might as well stick with his favourite
as they are both the same size.

# WHAT DO YOU SEE, A VASE OR TWO FACES?

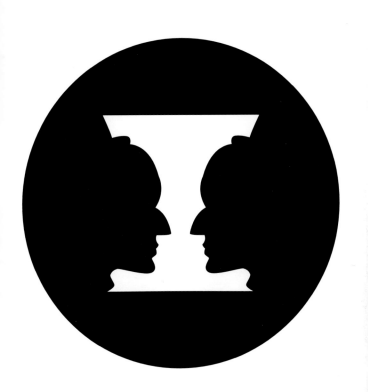

48

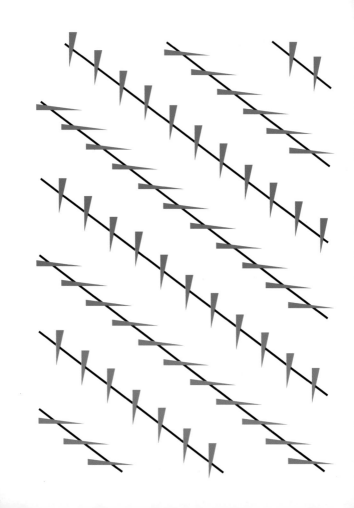

## ARE ANY OF THE LONG LINES PARALLEL?

Actually they all are but our judgement
is distorted by the short lines which
criss-cross them. This is an example
of a Hering Illusion.

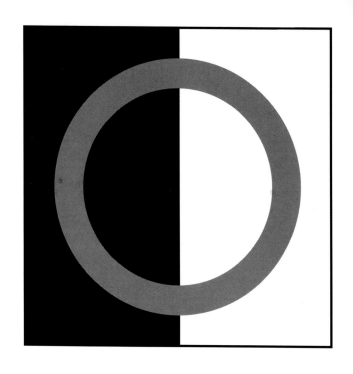

WHICH AREAS OF GREY ARE THE DARKEST?

They are all exactly the same shade but they look different due to the contrasting backgrounds.

# STARE AT THE CROSS BENEATH THE CIRCLE...

...for about 45 seconds, then stare at the cross between the squares. After a while, the top square should appear smaller than the bottom square.

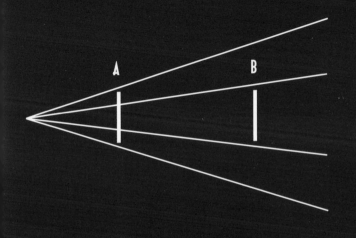

## WHICH IS SMALLER, A OR B?

FOR SOME REASON, MOST PEOPLE SEE PALE COLOURS IN TWO OF THESE SQUARES. WHICH SQUARES VARIES FROM PERSON TO PERSON.

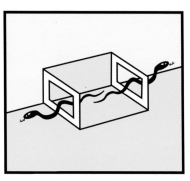

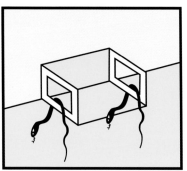

IS THE BOX RESTING ON THE FLOOR OR
HANGING FROM THE CEILING?

# I
# LOVE
# PARIS IN THE
# THE SPRINGTIME

WHAT DOES THIS SAY?
ARE YOU SURE?

58

# AN IMPOSSIBLE CRATE!

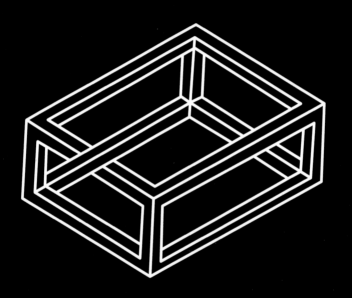

60

# ARE THESE HORIZONTAL LINES PARALLEL?

It's hard to believe, but they are. This is another example of a Hering Illusion.

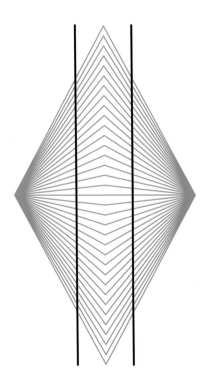

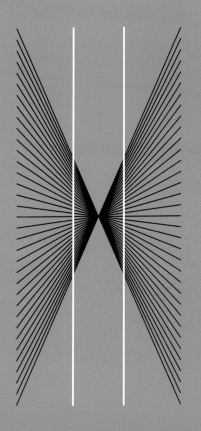

62

# ARE THESE CIRCLES DISTORTED?

No. They are perfect, but the diagonal line
pattern appears to bend them.

Stare at this design and lots of white spots will appear amongst the black ones. Move your eyes and they will disappear.

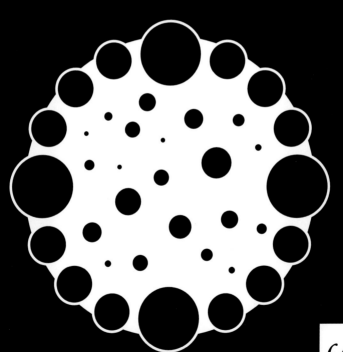

# ARE THESE LETTERS STRAIGHT?

Although they may look as if an electric current has passed through them, hold the page at arm's length and squint and the letters become upright and parallel to one another.

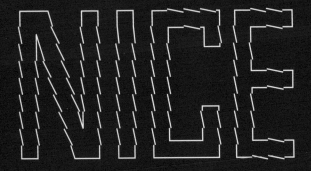

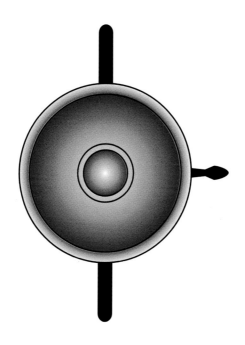

## WHAT IS THIS?

A bird's-eye view of a Mexican on a bike, indicating right.

66

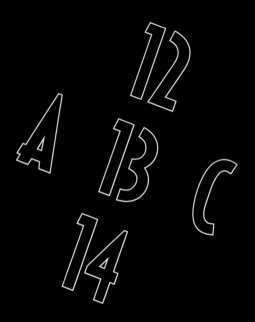

DO YOU READ THE LETTER **B** OR THE NUMBER **13**?

# FUNKY GRIDS

If you stare at these grids, you will soon start to see grey spots appearing at the intersections. As soon as you try to focus on them, they disappear.

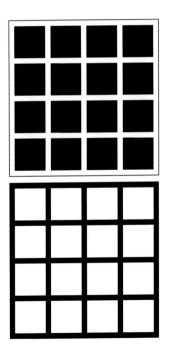

# WHO DO YOU SEE?

"My husband and my father-in-law" by
Jack Botwinick (1961).

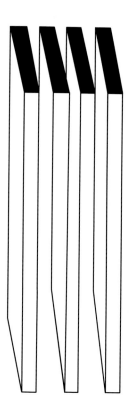

HOW MANY PLANKS ARE THERE, 3 OR 4?

# WHAT CAN YOU SEE IN THIS PICTURE?

It's a man kneeling. Once we see the image, we never have the same problem of interpretation again.

# WHAT IS THIS?

A giraffe walking past a high window.

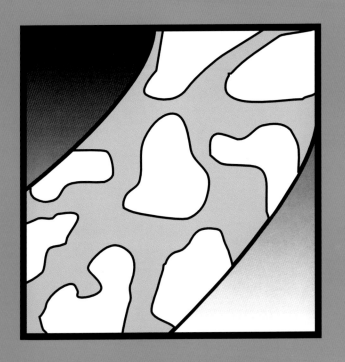

# WHICH FENCE IS LONGER?

## A

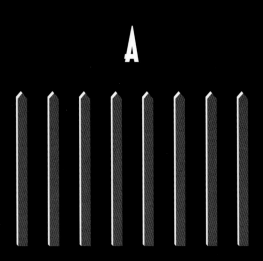

You may have less posts to paint on fence B, but both fences cover the same amount of ground.

B

# HAS THIS STAIRCASE BEEN DRAWN THE RIGHT WAY UP?

(Turn the book upside down to check)
Either way up is correct, for this is an example of
Schroder's reversible staircase.

# WHICH WALL WOULD YOU LEAST LIKE TO FALL OFF?

It will hurt either way, as they are both the same height!

# WHICH IMAGE DO YOU SEE?

A native American Indian or an
Eskimo looking into a cave?

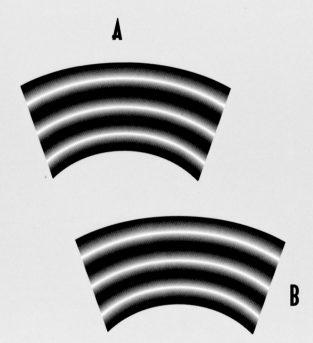

A

B

# WOULD YOU NEED TO GO FURTHER IN SEARCH OF THE POT OF GOLD AT THE END OF RAINBOW B?

No, both rainbows are exactly the same size.

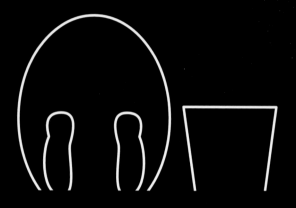

## WHAT IS THIS?

A washerwoman with her bucket.

# Is the brim of Aunt Agnes' hat as wide as the hat is high?

Astonishingly it is! People think that the hat is higher than it is wide because we are inclined to over-estimate the length of vertical lines when compared to horizontal ones.

84

# WOULD YOU BELIEVE A HANDYMAN WHO TOLD YOU THAT ALL THESE TILES THAT HE FIXED WERE PERFECTLY STRAIGHT?

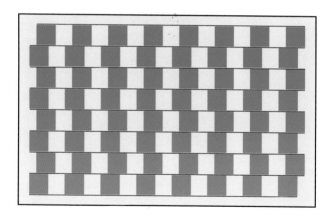

Although they look higgledy-piggledy, he would be telling the truth. The lines are parallel and the tiles even.

# ARE THERE SIX OR SEVEN STACKED CUBES?

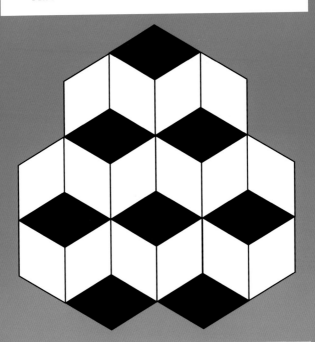

There are six cubes if you count the dark diamonds as the top of the cubes and seven if you count them as the base.

DO YOU SEE A TRIANGLE BELOW?
STRANGE, BECAUSE THERE'S NOT ONE THERE!

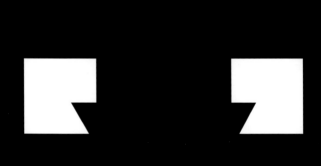

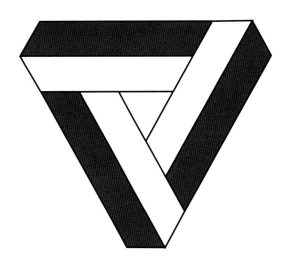

# THE PENROSE TRIANGLE

It's impossible to find your way around the triangle — the inside surface becomes the outside surface and vice versa.

**FURTHER READING:**

If you've enjoyed this book here are
some other excellent titles that
further investigate optical illusions.
The editors would like to thank the authors
of these works for the inspiration
that their books have provided.

**CAN YOU BELIEVE YOUR EYES?**
J Richard Block
Harold E Yuker
Robson Books 1991

**TAKE A CLOSER LOOK!**
Keith Kay
Bright Interval Books 1988

**EXPLORABOOK**
John Cassidy
The Exploratorium
Klutz Press 1991

**MIND SIGHTS**
Roger N Shepard
W H Freeman and Co. 1990

**THE EYE BEGUILED**
Bruno Ernst
Benedikt Taschen 1986

And also.....

**VISUAL GAMES** (Franco Agositini),
**ILLUSIONS** (Edi Lanners) &
**OPTICAL ILLUSIONS AND THE VISUAL ARTS**
(J B Thurston & R G Carraher).